Hymns of Hope and Healing

*Words and music to refresh
the church's ministry of healing*

Edited by Jan Berry & Andrew Pratt
with
Janet Eldred & Anne Sardeson

Stainer & Bell

First published in 2017 by
Stainer & Bell Limited, PO Box 110, Victoria House, 23 Gruneisen Road,
London N3 1DZ, England.

Cover illustration: *Incarnation*, an original watercolour © Andrew Pratt.
Reproduced by permission.
Back cover photograph: *Holy Rood House* © Ms Sandra Cockayne.
sandracockaynephotography.co.uk. Reproduced by permission.

British Library Cataloguing-in-Publication Data
A catalogue record of this book is available from the British Library

ISBN 978 0 85249 954 2

Printed in Great Britain by Caligraving Ltd, Thetford

CONTENTS

3 CHRIST THE HEALER

4 HEALING IN LIFE'S TRANSITIONS

5 SINGING OUR PRAYERS

INTRODUCTION

Hymns are powerful. For many people the words and tunes of particular hymns are resonant with memories, associations and strong feelings. The combination of verse and music, and the embodied singing with others, mean that words and their meanings linger in our subconscious, long after we have ceased to sing them or listen to them. Hymns have the power to speak to our deepest hurts, to give voice to our dreams, hopes and aspirations, and to affirm and encourage us as we encounter life's transitions and challenges. They have the power to help and to heal.

Holy Rood House, in Thirsk, Yorkshire, is a retreat and therapeutic centre. People who seek healing come there with their woundedness of many kinds. They come looking for space in which to rest and recover, from grief or from the exhaustion of caring. They come looking for wisdom and help as they face crises and difficult phases of their lives. They find healing, and a rhythm of worship and prayer undergirding their time of retreat and refreshment.

In 2010 the work of Holy Rood House gave birth to the Hymns for Healing project, an attempt to gather together theologians, biblical scholars, hymn-writers, musicians and all who delight in hymns, to explore the many ways in which this unique combination of words and music contributes to the ministry of healing. Funded by the Pratt Green Trust, the project ran a number of residential workshops and day events, looking at various aspects of hymnody and hymn-writing. As well as the craft of hymn-writing, we explored issues of images of healing, the impact of modern technologies and medical advances, hymns relating to ageing and dementia – and always included space for new writing and composition.

In many ways, hymns work because of their familiarity, their associations and the memories they hold. There is a continuing place for well-loved hymns; but we also became aware, through the project, of the need for new hymns relating to healing. For some, the word 'healing' carries associations of the miraculous and supernatural, of an interventionist God fixing what has gone wrong. We wanted to create hymns that spoke of healing in a more incarnational, embodied way – not as of a God 'out there' but a God with us in the process of healing. We wanted to sing of a holistic concept of healing, that embraced not just the physical but also the emotional and relational healing and growth that is a part of our human living. We wanted to acknowledge both the healing and the challenges to our concepts of health that come through advances in medicine and new technology. We wanted to affirm that healing is not restricted to individual human lives, but is needed at a social, political and environmental level. We wanted words that would give voice to the needs and hopes of those seeking healing beyond the walls of a church; and we wanted to recognise the questioning, pain and doubt when healing does not happen.

This book brings together some of the best writing from the project and beyond it. The collection includes new tunes and more familiar ones, words and their musical settings from a group of writers and composers ranging from the experienced to those making early attempts in the form. It includes hymns relating to personal healing, both physical and emotional, and to understandings of healing in today's world of politics and social justice, new technologies and environmental issues. It explores themes of healing in relation to the life, death and resurrection of Christ, and looks at how we grow towards wholeness in the transitions of life. It concludes with a section of short or repetitive texts to be used in conjunction with prayer.

It is our hope that this book will speak to the needs of many involved in chaplaincy, particularly in healthcare settings; that it will provide a vehicle for worship, prayer and reflection for those involved in therapies and counselling; that it will stimulate interest in healing in the wider church, for individuals and congregations alike; and, most of all, that it will offer hymns for all those who share a desire and passion to re-imagine and refresh the church's ancient ministry of healing.

Jan Berry

Hymns of Hope
and Healing

1

HEALING IN OUR LIVES

The concept of healing is ever-present in our lives, in the context of a scientific world-view dominated by the success of evidence-based medicine. Conception can take place in-vitro, outside the womb. We can perform surgery on a foetus before birth. Our DNA can be decoded, manipulated, repaired. We can extend life as never before. All of this has led us to a perception that there is no ailment potentially beyond our powers of healing, and even death may be delayed, if not avoided.

However, we are mortal, subject to hurt, harm and decay. Death, our own death and the disappearance of all whom we love, is inescapable, and immortality an illusion. For this reason the hymns in this section take a realistic view of healing. Even if many medical phenomena once classed as mysterious or even miraculous can now be rationally explained, there are still vast areas beyond our understanding. Whether as individuals or social creatures, our future is uncertain; and at some point in each of our lives we shall experience death, bereavement and loss.

These hymns will, it is hoped, strengthen us in our ability to live our mortal lives even amidst all their predicaments, in the knowledge that in sickness it is human hands and love that may be the means of divine intervention, enabling us to cope. For example, waking from an operation may be experienced as a resurrection. Then, at the last, we shall still be held by an expansive love, even when we cannot and will not wake to a new dawn.

A hymn of welcome

1   We reach for a welcome that beckons us homeward,
       crossing the threshold to find safer space,
       a place we can turn to in hurt and rejection,
       where tender compassion bears witness to grace.

       We rest in a love that can offer us healing,
       care for the aching and comfort for pain,
       a gentle embrace of our wounds and our rawness,
       protecting our frailty through suffering and strain.

       We long for a wisdom that answers our searching,
       the questions that baffle and agonised cries,
       the mystery behind all our anger and stumbling
       in darkness that hides all the path from our eyes.

       We sing of a hope that is flourishing in us,
       shaping our lives into all they might be,
       delighting in art and in music and laughter,
       the God of creation in joy sets us free.

       Jan Berry (1953–)

Metre: 12.11.12.11.
Tune: HOLY ROOD HOUSE
Alternative Tune: STREETS OF LAREDO

HOLY ROOD HOUSE

Valerie Ruddle (1932–)

We reach for a wel-come that beck - ons us home-ward, cross - ing the thres-hold to find sa - fer space, a place we can turn to in hurt and re - jec - tion, where ten - der com - pas - sion bears wit - ness to grace.

In times of uncertainty

2   When the future's all uncertain
and the path is so unsure,
then I know you'll show the way to me,
for you've been there before.

When a friend is deeply troubled,
with emotions red and raw,
then I know you'll give the words to me
for you've felt grief before.

When someone close is suffering
and there seems to be no cure,
then I know you'll pray the prayer for me,
for you've known pain before.

So when life is like a quicksand,
and I do not feel secure,
then I know you'll be a rock for me,
for you've been there before.

Anne Mott (1938–)

Metre: 8.7.9.6.
Tune: YOU'VE BEEN THERE BEFORE

YOU'VE BEEN THERE BEFORE

Anne Mott (1938–)

When the fu - ture's all un - cer - tain and the

path is so un - sure, then I know you'll show the

way to me, for you've been there be - fore.

When faith is clinging on

3   Sometimes our grasp of life is frail,
yet through it all love will prevail.
And when it seems things can't get worse,
we feel that every step is cursed.

In spite of all, we keep our faith,
held, more than holding on to grace,
we whisper prayer and hope for praise,
we live through grey exhausting days.

God's word reminds of how we're held,
when love is hidden, faith is felled;
retelling narratives of pain
from which God's people rose again.

This is the hope to which we cling,
when life is raw, we sense death's sting;
yet on beyond this time and place
may we be kept within your grace.
Amen.

Andrew Pratt (1948–)

Metre: LM
Suggested Tune: GONFALON ROYAL

When God seems absent

4   From the depths my voice had echoed,
       prayers were flung against the void,
       to my mind hope seemed to founder,
       faith it seemed had been destroyed.

       So in this distress I waited,
       God seemed absent, gone away,
       darkness shrouded every moment,
       guilt had clouded every day.

       Yet while feeling God-forsaken
       love had found me where I fell,
       healed the hurt of my existence,
       sought me out and made me well.

       Andrew Pratt (1948–)

© Copyright 2012 Stainer & Bell Ltd

Metre: 8.7.8.7.
Suggested Tune: ALL FOR JESUS

In times of loss

5   God, hold us, enfold us, through desolate loss.
The sign of your love is your own empty cross.
The shock and the anger, the hopeless despair
are echoes of Calvary. God, meet us there!

God, hold us, enfold us, through long empty days,
when living is pointless, a meaningless maze.
We need you to listen to raging and tears,
to anguish and doubt, to remorse and to fears.

God, hold us, enfold us, by friends who can share
our sorrow and pain with compassionate care.
By their words, you speak out your loving concerns.
They hold us for you, while the tide of grief turns.

God, hold us, enfold us, till weeping has passed;
when flickering hope parts the shadows at last.
One step at a time you will help us to move
to face new horizons, held safe in your love.

Marjorie Dobson (1940–)

Metre: 11 11.11 11.
Suggested Tune: NORMANDY (Basque)

In times of illness

6 When the body's strength is failing
and our energy is drained,
all we'd planned and worked for fading,
faithful trust and hope are strained.

In our longing for an ending
to the anger, pain and tears,
you surround us with your tending,
holding us through doubt and fear.

In our wait for healing's wisdom,
we find silence, rest and space,
learning from the body's rhythm,
touched by moments of God's grace.

In the body's restoration
to a world we see anew,
we embrace our re-creation,
offering grateful praise to you.

Jan Berry (1953–)

Metre: 8.7.8.7.
Suggested Tunes: AE FOND KISS; ST ANDREW (Thorne)

In times of pain

7   When days are filled with pain,
when praying seems in vain
and the future is not plain –
ask God to hold you.

When life is going wrong,
when you feel you can't be strong
and for rest and peace you long –
ask God to hold you.

When hope that's been reborn
in the glory of a dawn
turns to darkness and you mourn –
ask God to hold you.

When deep in your despair,
when no one seems to care,
empty grief is all that's there –
ask God to hold you.

Then your prayer will bring release
and though heartache may not cease,
with his love and strength and peace
God will enfold you.

Jean Bright (1932–)

Metre: 6 6 7.5.
Tune: COMPASSION

COMPASSION

Valerie Ruddle (1932–)

When days are filled with pain, when pray-ing seems in vain and the

fu - ture is not plain – ask God to hold_____ you.

Thanksgiving for hospital or healthcare staff

8   We owe our lives to those who care
          without discrimination,
          who offer comfort, kindness, skill:
          a present incarnation.

          When wakeful in the dead of night
          with pain our sole companion,
          you minister with human hands,
          you share in fear's dark canyon.

          A present promise of your love,
          you come with grace abounding,
          another morning wakes to sight,
          and praise may yet be sounding!

          Andrew Pratt (1948–)

Metre: 8.7.8.7.
Suggested Tune: DOMINUS REGIT ME

For times of rest and retreat

9 Through this day of quiet and calm
let your peace sink into my soul.
In this place, with time out of time,
send your grace that I may be whole.

In my world of day-to-day cares,
stress and strain can trouble my mind.
Here today, God, grant me the space;
calm my fears and help me unwind.

God, who spoke to waken the world,
speak today with challenge and choice.
Touch my life with wisdom and power.
Let me catch the tone of your voice.

Marjorie Dobson (1940–)

Metre: LM
Suggested Tune: SCARBOROUGH FAIR

In times of delight and faith

10   Delight in what I give:
                this ground to rest and be.
            All hell breaks loose within your soul;
                no words will set you free.
            Yet here, beneath your feet,
                you'll find I've always been:
            a constant, rooting, growing ground,
                unbidden and unseen.

            Delight in what I give:
                a life that loves you still.
            Chaotic doubt invades your mind;
                no words will calm your will.
            Yet here, encircling round,
                you'll find I've always been:
            a constant, loving, listening life,
                unbidden and unseen.

            Delight in what I give:
                a truth in all you do.
            For fear and torment fill your thoughts;
                no words will now ring true.
            So here, to calm your soul,
                you'll find I've always been:
            a constant, feeding, skilful truth,
                unbidden and unseen.

            Delight in where I lead:
                a way that knows no bound.
            When certainty is all you crave
                look up, see what is found.
            For here, beyond your sight,
                you'll find I've also been:
            a constant, calling, weaving way,
                unbidden and unseen.

            Anne Sardeson (1966–)

Metre: SMD
Tune: FAITH'S DELIGHT

FAITH'S DELIGHT

Anne Sardeson (1966–)

Delight in what I give: this ground to rest and be. All hell breaks loose with-in your soul; no words will set you free. Yet here, be-neath your feet, you'll find I've al-ways been: a constant, root-ing, grow-ing ground, un-bid-den and un-seen.

Self-acceptance

11   We are who we are, the tears and the laughter,
all woven together, all giving us life!
We are who we are, and God is here with us
when hope is abundant, when fear is rife.

So wait here and wonder for God's word this day.
Come ponder and treasure the things God will say.

We are who we are, the snags and dropped stitches,
the weaving and pulling together give breath.
We are who we are, and God weaves despite us
and for us and with us, in life and in death.

So wait here and wonder for God's word this day.
Come ponder and treasure the things God will say.

We are who we are, and God is here calling,
not calling perfection, but calling what is.
We come as we are, and deep in our being
our spirit is stirred, and finds God is all this!

Anne Sardeson (1966–)

Metre: 11.11.11.11. and Refrain
Tune: BEING

BEING

Anne Sardeson (1966–)

For difficult debates and decisions

12   Looking at life: connecting with passion
all that divides, all things that unite;
hoping beyond all that we bring here,
daring to hold God in our sight.

Sharing with pain: waiting for wisdom;
some things destroy, some things build worth.
Gracing the pain a spirit is stirring:
do we dare wait for the life it will birth?

Moving beyond: emerging in tears;
life that looks back, life that grows on.
Never forget the hope that conceived you:
ever the search, ever God's song.

Anne Sardeson (1966–)

Thinking about the healing of relationships, and written while involved in the ongoing (and unresolved) discussion about human sexuality and the church.

Metre: 10.8.10.8.
Tune: WESTMINSTER COLLEGE

WESTMINSTER COLLEGE

Anne Sardeson (1966–)

Look-ing at life: con- -nect-ing with pas-sion all that div-ides, all things that u-nite; hop-ing be-yond all that we bring here, dar-ing to hold God in our sight.

* The voice may be doubled by flute.

© Copyright 2017 Stainer & Bell Ltd

Travelling on life's journey

13   *Travel with us at a pace that you're ready for;*
           no one will rush you or tell you 'slow down'.
           Here among friends is the gentlest of healing,
           to talk with companions or have time alone.

           We follow a God who holds all of our memories,
           meets us in sorrow and touches our pain.
           It's OK to weep when we're grieving or hurting:
           God's comfort will find us and love us again.

           So let's travel along at a pace that we're easy with,
           no one to rush us or make us go slow.
           Here among friends we find love and acceptance
           for all that we have been and all that we know.

           While children are running and young people dancing,
           we wait with respect while a mother gives birth.
           Then laugh and give thanks as we welcome the newcomer,
           letting her find her own space on the earth.

           As we travel with God in the joy that the Spirit gives,
           welcoming others with hearts open wide,
           here is an arm of support when there's need for it,
           here a companion to walk by your side.

           Then as the sun sets, we can gather in company,
           bring out the food and the wine for the feast.
           God's covenant binds us in love and humanity,
           sharing the good gifts that God has released.

           Janet Wootton (1952–)

Metre: 12.10.12.10. and 13.10.13.10.
Suggested Tune: BLOW THE WIND SOUTHERLY

Celebrating Christa

14   I promise you, my Christa, that I will always be
your wild and loving sister, who's learning to be free.
I'll dance the steps you've taught me, I'll walk the way you show,
and deep within my body your wisdom I will know.
I'll live through hurt and struggle, I'll share your loss and pain;
and bearing marks of suffering, with you I'll rise again.

For we are risen Christa, creating jubilee;
we're wild and daring women, delighting to be free.
We'll dance with gay abandon, we'll walk the living way,
and in our fleshly bodies, true beauty we'll display.
Not bound by words or dogma, elusive or unknown,
defying all conventions, we'll make the world our own.

Jan Berry (1953–)

The term 'Christa' denotes the attempt by feminist theologians, artists and poets to envisage a female Christ figure. See, for example, Nicola Slee, 'Seeking the Risen Christa' (SPCK, 2011). This hymn was written at a weekend with that title led by Nicola at Holy Rood House in June 2012, also the year of royal jubilee.

Metre: 13 13.13 13.13 13.
Suggested Tune: THAXTED

A prayer for the Spirit's inspiration

15   Jesus is healing care,
mother's love healing scars.
Arms to hold, words to share,
wrap us in your kindness,
let us be your likeness.

Spirit, come, come, come!
Spirit, come, come, come!
Comfort us,
cherish us,
and inspire with beauty!

Mother God, hold our pain,
mapping out new terrain,
deep down be more humane.
Let us feel uplifted,
knowing how we're gifted.
Refrain

Father God, help us bring
much new love to our kin.
As we face strange new things
give shape to our living,
make us kind in giving.
Refrain

Loving God, hear our prayer,
as we face new despair.
When we feel life's unfair,
guide us through; astound us!
Let us know you've found us!
Refrain

Eagle God, lift us high!
Fledglings we cannot fly,
little wings, aiming high.
Have with us strong patience.
Let us be courageous.
Refrain

Sara Iles (1967–)

Inspired by Deuteronomy 32:11 – 'As an eagle stirreth up her nest, fluttereth over her young, spreadeth abroad her wings, taketh them, beareth them on her wings' (KJV).

Metre: 6 6 6.6 6. and Refrain
Suggested Tune: PERSONENT HODIE (THEODORIC)

Travelling on life's path

16   O Gracious God, your love for us is yearning,
deep in our hearts, you still our doubts and fears;
blessing with love, so great and so abundant,
words of forgiveness, heal our deepest hurt.
Come now and rest your blessing in our Spirit;
come now and rest your blessing in our hearts;
you are our God, and we your loving children,
who travel on life's path and find in you our goal.

O Jesus Christ, you walk this earth, as we do,
making us whole, with every step you take;
teaching all people with the words of healing,
and reaching outward to the lost and loved.
Come now and challenge all our social boundaries;
come now and challenge all that comfort brings;
you are our God and we your loving children,
who travel on life's path, abundant with your love.

O Holy Spirit, breathing through creation,
touching all life with energising power;
guiding us through the trials and temptations
that block our journey on our way to God.
Come now and breathe your gentle breath, enfold us;
come now and breathe your comfort when it hurts;
you are our God and we your loving children,
who travel on life's path, to our eternal home.

Ruth Dillon (1956–)

Metre: 11.10.11.10.11.10.11.12.
Suggested Tune: LONDONDERRY AIR

A prayer for healing

17   God, who has made us both body and soul,
        Jesus, who made our humanity whole,
        Spirit, who lightens our lives with your fire,
        hear when we pray for the things we desire,
        and grant us the healing we need.

        Some of us wake every morning to pain;
        ailing or ageing, our bodies complain;
        some will be patient while others despair.
        God, as you never give up on your care,
        please grant us the healing we need.

        Some live with demons we carry within,
        whether as sinners or victims of sin,
        plagued by the bitterness, tempted to hate.
        God, who forgave though your anguish was great,
        please grant us the healing we need.

        All of us know we are mortal and frail,
        yet we believe that your love will not fail.
        Through all the troubles and trials that we face,
        help us to trust in your ultimate grace
        to grant us the healing we need.

        Sue Gilmurray (1950–)

Metre: 10 10.10 10.8.
Tune: THE HEALING WE NEED

THE HEALING WE NEED

Sue Gilmurray (1950–)

God, who has made us both bo - dy and soul,

Je - sus, who made our hu - ma - ni - ty whole,

Spi - rit, who light - ens our lives with your fire,

hear when we pray for the things we de - sire, and

grant us the heal - ing we need.

Comfort in our brokenness

18   In brokenness we bring to you
         a world of suffering and pain.
         We search for comfort in your touch,
         to heal and make us whole again.

         And some are trapped in darkened minds;
         no room for light or hope or prayer.
         Yet down among the graves we see
         you drive out demons of despair.

         Restored to mental health and peace,
         the journey back becomes our goal,
         the chains of darkness left behind,
         restored and loved and healed and whole.

         Carolyn Sanderson (1948–)

Metre: LM
Suggested Tunes: HAVEN (Howarth); HERONGATE

Confidence in God's healing

19   When the body's racked with pain,
treatments all applied in vain,
dare to think a cure remains:
God's love can heal us.

When the spirit's crushed or torn,
when no joy comes with the dawn,
seek the gift of hope reborn:
God's love can heal us.

When the flower of friendship dies,
through suspicion, fear or lies,
hear the voice that calms our cries:
God's love can heal us.

When the nations come to blows,
turning friends to murderous foes,
even faced with such great woes,
God's love can heal us.

When our course is nearly run,
when the thread of life is spun,
fear not what's been left undone.
God's love will heal us.

Stephen Linstead (1941–)

Metre: 7 7 7.5.
Suggested Tune: CA' THE EWES

A lament in times of anger

20   When frustration feeds our anger,
hatred is too soft a word,
can you hear our cries of anguish?
Is our question just absurd?

Yes, the psalmist ransacked language,
mined the phrases that would cry
out of depths of human raging
every scream and every sigh.

Ageless God, we need your promise
that in spite of all we feel,
you will take us and enfold us,
hear and comfort, hold and heal.

Andrew Pratt (1948–)

Metre: 8.7.8.7.
Suggested Tune: LOVE DIVINE (Stainer)

Loneliness and isolation

21   When loneliness oppresses me;
when darkness fills my soul;
when grief and weeping overwhelm
and none can make me whole;
in angry fear I call to you.
When will you hear my cry?
This heavy burden on my heart
must lift, or else I die.

When close companions melt away,
afflictions have no end,
I cry for help to empty air,
darkness my only friend.
O God, why have you left me here?
When will my troubles cease?
If you refuse to hear my prayer,
how will I find release?

Marjorie Dobson (1940–)

Based on Psalm 88.

Metre: CMD
Suggested Tune: KINGSFOLD

Confronting our mortality

22   Our lives are finite yet we strive.
We cannot trust the signs we see,
that being has a natural end:
the waning of humanity.
The protestation of our faith,
that resurrection quells our fear,
feels hollow as our grief grows deep,
while tears will tantalise and sear.

From birth the certainty is death,
the single truth we cannot change,
and yet we struggle to ignore
this certain void that seems so strange.
Accepting this it seems absurd
to try to struggle with the flow.
A kinder way might seem to be
to walk together as we go.

Perhaps this is the greatest truth:
that healing can evade our grasp,
yet calm acceptance of this fact
can bring shalom, and peace will last.
No rage against the dying light,
nor expectation of the morn,
but simple, calm, accepting love
to hold us when there is no dawn.

Andrew Pratt (1948–)

Metre: LMD
Suggested Tunes: YE BANKS AND BRAES; BEFORE THE THRONE

The power of touch

23   Touch, without words, a silent understanding
that reaches deep within another's pain,
can bring the present healing to our being,
a sense of peace, though hurt may still remain.
And in this touch God's love, a bridge between us,
can form a bond that words cannot express,
can draw us in communion with each other,
can ease and share the things that bring distress.

The things we hold in common hold us closer,
we learn to weep together, share our tears,
while love, the distillation of compassion
will bring a sense of grace to quell our fears.
God's touch is constant, though the world is changing.
God's love is present, loving will remain.
However much security may crumble,
God's patient grace and hope will still sustain.

Andrew Pratt (1948–)

Metre: 11.10.11.10.D.
Suggested Tune: LONDONDERRY AIR

A hope of resurrection

24   Each hour marks a mighty resurrection,
a time of overcoming fate and fear,
the dawning of a common understanding
in which the grace of God is drawing near.

Each morning brings a sense of new creation.
New life, new love, encompasses the earth.
New time, new light illuminates the distance,
as though the world is coming, fresh, to birth.

Each evening brings a stunning revelation,
as stars and planets hove into our view,
beyond imagination and reflection,
these scattered bangles flung against the blue.

Each season brings a sense of co-existence,
relatedness of heartbeat, rhythm, rhyme;
and every year the cycle goes on spinning,
affirming faith and love through endless time.

Andrew Pratt (1948–)

Metre: 11.10.11.10.
Suggested Tune: HIGHWOOD

2

HEALING IN TODAY'S WORLD

There is surely today a popular assumption, fostered by ideals of scientific progress, that no affliction is beyond healing, given sufficient time and money in the search for a cure. And yet we are still accompanied by our human vulnerability and hubris, as the ever-increasing concerns about the dangers of antibiotic resistance testify. As humanity evolves, so too do those organisms that can infect, disrupt and potentially destroy it. Contrary to the optimistic assumptions made by some commentators, it is more likely that disease in one form or another will always be with us. In addition, successive generations will have an increased capacity to enhance or denigrate the environment. Those very technologies that have improved the quality of our existence can also be detrimental to the natural world for generations to come.

In all of this there is a need to address healing in a way which is realistic for our own lives. What cannot be avoided is the question of theodicy: the problem of evil in the context of a world created and held in existence by a God of love. In this light, we have explored the place of scientific discovery and technological application in healthcare, together with the continuing need for compassion and the human touch.

In a wider context there are also texts exploring disastrous natural phenomena of global impact, earthquakes and tsunamis, that exist as a consequence of the structure of our planet and, arguably, have proved essential for life even to have existed here.

Political choices and international relations enable or undermine our capacity to bring healing and shalom on a global scale. Often politicians are making economic choices between those areas of expense which have the capacity to destroy life, and those which can enhance and heal.

Hymns here begin to touch the surface of the exploration of these different themes of genomes and geology, of economics and politics, of conservation and environment, and our place and purpose in the whole process of existence.

Research and exploration

25   God who drives our exploration
           past old limits of the mind
           into realms of comprehension
           new and strange to humankind,
           when our world is changed for ever
           by the power of new ideas
           may we balance innovation
           with the wisdom of the years.

           Living tissue holds potential
           greater than we dared to dream,
           so that shattered minds and bodies
           walk and breathe and speak again.
           Stem cells offer hope for healing
           where there was no hope before –
           help us grasp the consequences
           waiting through each open door.

           Sequencing the human genome
           offers hope to find the means
           to eradicate conditions
           written into people's genes,
           guarding future generations,
           who will never know the cost,
           from inherited diseases,
           of the lives that have been lost.

           When research leads into places
           that we cannot understand,
           hold us back from mindless judgments,
           or from 'healing on demand'.
           Strengthen those who face decisions
           greater than their hearts can bear,
           holding life and death in balance,
           weighing what is just and fair.

           Janet Wootton (1952–)

Metre: 8.7.8.7.D.
Suggested Tunes: STRANMILLS; HEANISH

Thanksgiving for birth, life and death

26　　Give thanks to God for miracles of birth.
A mother weeps for joy to see her child:
a skilful surgeon healed him in the womb –
he's in an incubator, not a tomb.

Give thanks to God for miracles of life;
for joy and laughter and for pain and tears.
We long for healing for all troubled lands
and offer life and help with open hands.

Give thanks to God for miracles of death,
the final healing: earthly pain is past.
God's faithful people feel his welcome grace
and weep with joy to see Christ face to face.

Jean Wiggins (1937–)

Metre:　　　10.10.10 10.
Suggested Tune:　SURSUM CORDA (Smith)

Researching an illness or medical condition

27   Virtual God, I am surfing,
       looking for your healing grace;
       wishing that I could press enter
       and see your face.

       When I research this condition,
       how do I know what is true?
       How do I recognise wisdom?
       God, where are you?

       Everything happened so quickly,
       where is the time to adjust?
       Help me escape this new illness –
       in God I trust.

       Out of the depths I am calling,
       come to me quickly as light,
       give me a vision of wholeness.
       Please, put me right!

       Comforter, cleanser and healer,
       Jesus, companion and friend,
       God of compassion and mercy,
       when will it end?

       Diane Coleman (1947–)

Metre: 8.7.8.4.
Tune: VIRTUAL VOICES

VIRTUAL VOICES

Nicholas Williams (1959–)

The wonders and dilemmas of medical technology

28 Give praise for the wonder encoded in genes,
the probing to learn what our DNA means,
the searching for answers, the passion to know
what causes our life-force to flourish and grow.

As research increases our technique and skill
we face the dilemmas, to withhold or heal.
Our expanding knowledge creates shape and form
as patterns of birthing and dying transform.

When organs are failing and bodies despair
the crisis of transplant gives hope of repair –
the marvels of drugs and the skill of the knife,
the tools of the experts that offer new life.

The magic of science enchants with its spell,
enticing with promise of 'All shall be well',
O God who inhabits our bodies and breath,
enfold us with wisdom to meet life and death.

Jan Berry (1953–)

Metre: 11 11.11 11.
Tune: KILNER
Alternative Tune: ST DENIO

KILNER

Sue Gilmurray (1950–)

Give praise for the won - der en - cod-ed in genes, the prob - ing to learn what our D N A means, the search - ing for ans - wers, the pas-sion to know＿ what caus-es our life - force to flour-ish and grow. As wis - dom＿ to meet life and death.

The wonders of scientific discovery

29   Creative wisdom of our God,
delightful planner, who designed
an intricate, amazing world
to dazzle and compel the mind:

We honour those who dared to probe
below the surface of our sight,
whose diligent researches brought
a microscopic world to light.

Compassion drove a search for truth
to build on their discoveries
with new procedures and techniques
and fight the causes of disease.

Prophetic voices raised a call
for justice at the point of need,
a challenge to a world where health
is prisoner to human greed.

God, let your wisdom lead the way
through explorations of the mind,
and may compassion free us for
the wonders we have yet to find.

Janet Wootton (1952–)

Metre: LM
Suggested Tune: TALLIS' CANON

Taking up the cross

30   Take up your cross and follow me!
Dare risk upsetting powers-that-be –
the forces shaping life and thought;
expose the webs in which we're caught.

Take up your cross at one with those
whose role as scapegoats grows and grows;
so love 'the least', who give, give, give –
those asked to die before they live.

Take up your cross – the Empire's tool –
though it may make you seem a fool;
but not to bless the fear it spreads,
instead to drain its poisoned threads:

Denounce the lie that 'might is right';
that says the poor deserve their plight.
Take up your cross and follow me:
the kingdom's truth shall set you free!
Amen.

Graham Adams (1975–)

Metre: LM
Suggested Tune: GONFALON ROYAL

A celebration of openness and welcome

31   There is no place in God's household
for the sly deceiver's voice,
no room left for false entrapment
snaring those who have no choice.
There is room for honest welcome,
for rebuilding shattered dreams
where the lost can find a way back
from their tangled web of schemes.

There is no place in God's household
for the pall of secrecy,
no room left to skulk in corners
hiding what we fear to see.
There is room for honest speaking,
crying 'Justice!', weeping tears,
where the lost can find their freedom
in a place that knows their fears.

God of justice, God of freedom,
in your household, there is space
filled with light and hope and laughter
rich with love and healing grace.
There you offer royal welcome,
where no harm or hurt is found,
and we come in peace together,
for we stand on holy ground.

Janet Wootton (1952–)

Metre: 8.7.8.7.D.
Suggested Tune: LLANSANNAN

For justice in the city

32   With bodies for sale as they numb up the mind,
on streets or on screens they are easy to find;
they're stoned because that is the way they can bear
anonymous sex for the ones that don't care.

It's cold economics to be on the game;
it's cold prostitution, no love and no name.
Abusers abuse the abused all the night,
with no one to care if it's wrong or it's right.

These streets and these people God left in our care.
We know we should act, and we know we should dare
to tackle the pimping, the fear and the pain;
but can't beat the guardians of financial gain.

Society's driven by money and wealth:
who cares if it's greedy, injurious to health?
'But we are yours, Lord, and to you come to pray
that you'll act as God: make it all go away!'

God asks us to work so that justice is done;
and exploited children of God have begun
to value their bodies and lives, and to see
their worth in the Body of Christ, loved and free.

Damian Boddy (1948–)

Metre: 11 11.11 11.
Suggested Tune: MUELLER (also known as MANGER SCENE)

After urban violence and rioting

33   When law and trust break down,
          God, give us strength to cope;
          and in the heartache of our loss
          show us a sign of hope.

          When all around is hate,
          and voices cry in fear,
          God of our streets and urban life,
          come, dwell amongst us here.

          When beauty is destroyed
          and pride gives way to shame,
          in our bewilderment and pain,
          we call your holy name.

          When empty streets are dead,
          and smoke pervades the night,
          God, reach into our troubled hearts
          and bring us safe to light.

          When morning brings new calm,
          the debris washed with rain,
          as people clear the scattered shards,
          God, help us build again.

          Jan Berry (1953–)

Written after violent disturbances in English towns and cities in 2011.

Metre: SM
Tune: MONICA
Alternative Tune: SORROW

MONICA

June Boyce-Tillman (1943–)

When law and trust break down, God, give us strength to cope; and in the heart - ache of our loss show us a sign of hope. -gain.

Seeking God's presence in deprivation

34   Where is God when lives seem aimless,
kicking empty cans about?
Where is God if they're avoiding
homes that always shut them out?

Where is God when people queuing
for a brew are short of change?
Where is God when airborne bottles
find their human prey in range?

Where is God when desperate addicts
rob the weak of rings and pride?
Where is God if life in prison
teaches yet more ways inside?

Where is God when single parents
meet eviction in the face?
Where is God when teens in trouble
are not given time or space?

Where is God when racist taunting
turns the fear in 'us' on 'them'?
Where is God if half-truth tabloids
make us hastily condemn?

Where is God but in each question,
in the prompting us to care
how our lives might start to answer
those who ask 'Is God still there?'

Graham Adams (1975–)

Metre: 8.7.8.7.
Suggested Tune: CROSS OF JESUS

For refugees

35   We sit with bruised and broken souls
and watch our peace depart.
The grief of loss of innocence
has torn us all apart.
They came on boats to find a home
that wasn't filled with fear.
How many found a watery grave –
for them, there's no peace here.

The image of a little boy
asleep upon the sand
will stay for ever in our hearts,
a stain upon the land.
This tiny child has moved our world,
a seismic human-quake.
Once more it seems we needed death
to cause our hearts to wake.

May God's sweet child find peace at last –
but give no peace to those
who kill, despoil and terrorise:
for them no quiet repose.
Nor us – for there is work to do,
for we are duty bound
to strive for justice and for love
till peace for all is found.

Anna Jarvis (1976–)

The picture of the body of a refugee child washed up on a beach drew attention to the refugee crisis in 2015.

Metre: CMD
Suggested Tune: KINGSFOLD

God's love in brokenness and mending

36   The process of remaking
within the web of life
can set up new connections
to bring an end to strife.
The warmth of generous friendship
will soften walls of stone;
in breaking and in mending
the Love of God is known.

Abuse God-given freedom
through rape, injustice, greed –
this wounding of the fabric
will make God's body bleed.
In seeking out forgiveness
community is grown.
In breaking and in mending
the Love of God is known.

God's fingers gently weaving
within creation's heart
will sometimes pull together
and sometimes push apart;
and so the failing patterns
are carefully resewn.
In breaking and in mending
the Love of God is known.

God calls us to be weavers
and make the fabric strong
and wrestle with the shaping,
discerning right from wrong;
and so God's rainbow loving
within the cloth is shown.
In breaking and in mending
the Love of God is known.

June Boyce-Tillman (1943–)

Metre: 7.6.7.6.D.
Suggested Tune: AURELIA

Teaching and learning for the common good

37 Compassion flows and warms in our hearts,
calls upon us to free the earth.
The barriers fall; divisions end;
and everyone can claim their worth.
The poor can speak, the fearful stand,
the dispossessed can claim the hills;
and justice reigns and peace prevails,
reshaped through God's transforming skills.

And all shall teach the common good,
see that all life is interlinked;
the fertile soil will yield for all
life-giving food, reviving drink.
Respect for God, Creative Love,
will honour humans, trees and rocks,
build universities of hope
where Wisdom's power is unlocked.

And so we make our kinship here
echo the one that reigns in heaven,
where each is valued in God's love
and to that mercy says Amen.
The convicts leap, the outcasts dance,
the trapped throw off addiction's chains.
All sing in Christ the freedom song
created from our joys and pains.

June Boyce-Tillman (1943–)

For line 7, the rhythm of the second verse of the suggested tune should be substituted.

Metre: LMD
Suggested Tune: JERUSALEM (Parry)

A vision for the church

38   We dream of a church that will live as a movement
      set free from the boundaries and walls we create,
      and move towards Jesus who moves beyond borders
      to liberate people who dream as they wait.

      We dream of a church that will live out its story,
      proclaiming new life for earth's people this day;
      a church that re-learns its traditions of justice
      by sharing as equals and friends on the way.

      We dream of a church that will nurture potential,
      identify prejudice, conflict and fear,
      and strive for a world where we all work as partners
      by building God's future-koinonia* right here.

      We dream of a church that will risk reputation,
      compassion exceeding obsessions with gain;
      courageous in face of complacent resistance
      by caring for neighbours and outcasts the same.

      We dream of a church that will join with God's passion:
      may earth be restored and its peoples at peace!
      We trust as we journey without all the answers
      that God's love will guide us and hope shall not cease.

      Graham Adams (1975–)

* *'koinonia' [pronounced 'koy-no-nea'] is a Greek word which means fellowship or communion, partnership or solidarity – i.e. true community.*

Metre: 12.11.12.11.
Suggested Tune: STREETS OF LAREDO

Hope for the renewal of all creation

39 Within the pulsing universe God's Spirit gently flows,
restoring right connection through which creation grows;
with subtle understanding God takes each tiny part
and makes them fit together within a wounded heart.
We pray you, vibrant Spirit, infuse our hearts today
that we may act within you and understand your Way.

The joy of right relationship the cosmos can in-breathe,
as you encircle all things and lovingly re-weave
the strands of human living. The joy, disputes and pain
are taken and re-woven to make life flow again;
and we are called to do your work and make the weaving fair,
reflect your deep transforming love infusing all our care.

Our human institutions, our politics, our wealth
bear fruit in justice-making to serve a nation's health;
the difficult decisions – to nurture and control –
the maintenance of order and all that is involved
take place within your Wisdom still making all things new;
we ask that your amazing grace will fill all we pursue.

June Boyce-Tillman (1943–)

Metre: 14 13.13 13.13 13.
Suggested Tune: THAXTED

A prayer in times of disaster and terror

40   When earthquakes strike, and shake our sense of safety,
and turn communities to dust and tears;
when floods and hurricanes make people homeless,
we pray to God: 'Where are you in our fears?'

When conflict strikes and people run for refuge,
divided, crying 'Will we meet again?';
the threat of persecution, even torture,
prompts more lament: 'Where are you, God? Amen!'

When city bombs explode our long-held freedoms,
and home-grown violence greets us in the street;
we fear these things are signs our world is ending –
'Will we be saved from evils that we meet?'

But Christ has promised to be with us always,
especially where the people suffer most:
so when our human spirit learns compassion
in every earthquake Christ is then our Host.

Graham Adams (1975–)

Metre: 11.10.11.10.
Suggested Tune: INTERCESSOR

A prayer after a tsunami

41   Tectonic plates beneath the ocean's surface
uplifted, twisting life and limb and wave.
The landscape that was home has lost its features,
destruction means that few are left to save.

An empty chair amid such devastation
where cars like toys are lifted, spun about;
and here we wait and pray in helpless anguish;
and 'Where is God?' we want to cry and shout.

Incarnate God, we need your present spirit
to live within your people at this time,
to energise our prayerful words and action,
to offer grace to life's discordant rhyme.

God, offer hope to those who feel forsaken,
to those whose lives have spun and turned around;
to those whose grief defies all consolation,
bring grace and love and hope and solid ground.

Andrew Pratt (1948–)

Metre: 11.10.11.10.
Suggested Tune: LOMBARD STREET

The destruction of the earth and its need for healing

42   The earth calls out in hunger,
           the trees shout out in pain.
           Skies weep a thousand teardrops,
           tormenting fire will reign,
           for we, in human folly,
           in greed and ignorance,
           have trampled on God's garden
           and now the earth can't dance.

           With species dying daily
           and lakes and rivers dry,
           our oceans slowly poisoned,
           our barren hillsides sigh,
           while people sit in dustbowls,
           survival left to chance,
           when will that rhythm come that
           will help the world to dance?

           The planting of each sapling,
           the digging of each well,
           brings harvests of compassion
           and helps our music swell.
           We'll bring the earth our healing –
           we'll sing with confidence –
           our harmonies will join, and
           one day this earth will dance.

           Anna Jarvis (1976–)

Metre: 7.6.7.6.D.
Suggested Tune: CRÜGER

Creation and its healing

43   We listen with joy to the song of the morning
when angels rejoiced, and the skies came to birth;
when God placed the sun, moon and stars in the heavens,
shaped mountains and rivers and seas on the earth.

We dance in a world that is filled with God's glory,
of green growing beauty and creatures at play;
we laugh with its wonder and cry with its sorrow,
and rest in its quiet at the end of the day.

We weep for an earth that's in need of God's healing,
the oceans that roar and the rivers that cry;
we search for solutions, and shout out our questions
to God, who commands us to look to the sky.

We dream of a world that is living together,
with beauty and goodness and loving to share;
the answer God gives to our hope and our longing:
'The world that I fashioned is placed in your care.'

Jan Berry (1953–)

Metre: 12.11.12.11.
Suggested Tune: STREETS OF LAREDO

3

CHRIST THE HEALER

The Gospels are full of stories of Jesus's healing encounters with others: a feisty woman, a blind man of Bethsaida brought for healing, lepers shamed and outcast by their disease. Some of the hymns in this section recall and retell these stories, reminding us of a Jesus who healed and still continues to heal.

Healing is witnessed not only in the actual accounts of healing miracles, however, but is also encountered throughout the story of Jesus's life. These hymns also remind us of the waiting and hopefulness of Advent, and the disturbing joy of birth in a stable. They speak of sharing bread and wine at table, of the agony of crucifixion, and the wonder and joy of resurrection. The healing power of Christ is made real for us again as we sing our way through the Gospel story: through birth and life and ministry, through crucifixion and death, until we reach the joy of resurrection with 'alleluias ringing in delight'.

Advent

44   We wait in darkness for the dawn
         when night seems long and grey,
         the faintly gleaming ray of light
         that marks the edge of day.

         We wait in silence for the word
         that whispers in our ear,
         that gives our dreams a shape and form
         and gently calms our fear.

         We wait with patience for the time
         when healing comes again,
         while watching for the flickering signs
         of love's renewing reign.

         God waits with us in silent dark,
         in patience through the night,
         attending to our yearning dreams
         till hope comes with the light.

         Jan Berry (1953–)

Metre: CM
Suggested Tune: ST BOTOLPH (Slater)

Advent

45   See, she comes in expectation,
life within her blossoming;
new life growing, new life leaping
at her cousin's welcoming.
Alleluia, Alleluia, Alleluia:
let us join their flourishing.

Women meeting, women greeting,
sharing creativity,
telling stories, charting journeys,
blessing vulnerability.
Often weeping, often weeping, often weeping,
we guard their integrity.

Marks of birthing, scars of loving
in their bodies women bear,
holy markings, priestly scarring,
as they in love's passion share.
We with rapture, we with rapture, we with rapture
celebrate their birthing there.

Christ is nestling deep within us,
waiting for the time for birth.
Let us hold the Christ-light in us,
keep it rooted in the earth.
Come, Sophia, come, Sophia, come, Sophia,
rock us gently to rebirth.

June Boyce-Tillman (1943–)

Metre: 8.7.8.7.8.7. Extended
Suggested Tune: HELMSLEY

Advent/Christmas

46   If the Word becomes flesh then our life is worth living
If the Word dwells among us we touch hallowed ground

If the Word becomes flesh there is joy in our bodies
If the Word dwells among us we hear creation's voice

If the Word becomes flesh there is hope in our veins
If the Word dwells among us we will taste divinity

If the Word becomes flesh there is love on our streets
If the Word dwells among us we see the face of God

Anne Sardeson (1966–)

© Copyright 2017 Stainer & Bell Ltd

Tune: WORD BECOME FLESH

WORD BECOME FLESH

Anne Sardeson (1966–)

The tune should be sung unaccompanied.

© Copyright 2017 Stainer & Bell Ltd

Annunciation/Christmas

47   Young Mary, survivor, alone in the world,
        for that's how it seemed to the mind of this girl.
        An angel had promised the birth of a son,
        but Mary just wanted to hide or to run.

        Much less of a blessing, less joy to the earth,
        the sound to her ears of the promise of birth;
        unmarried, herself little more than a child,
        the thoughts in her mind were horrendous, ran wild.

        Would Joseph abandon her now in her need?
        Would he share the faith of our latter-day creed?
        More likely to leave her alone to her end,
        now wounded by bias, no longer her friend.

        That God could conceive to abandon, mistreat:
        a sordid beginning, a birth on the street;
        that Mary should taste wrath at such a young age;
        the cross threw its shadow across the world's stage.

        Before she could magnify God in her song,
        she had to confront all the world in its wrong,
        the things in her mind she could not reconcile,
        the world's misconceptions and Herod's cruel guile.

        We sing of a manger, we tell of a birth,
        our sentiment colours its moment and worth:
        as deity seems to collude with the state
        sing glory, sing Mary ... before it's too late.

        Andrew Pratt (1948–)

Metre: 11 11.11 11.
Tune: NORTH COUNTRY MAID
Alternative Tune: PADERBORN

NORTH COUNTRY MAID

Traditional English
Arranged Nicholas Williams (1959–)

Young Ma - ry, sur - vi - vor, a - lone in the world, for___

that's how it seemed to the mind of this girl. An_ an - gel had pro-mised the

birth_ of a son, but_ Ma - ry just want - ed to hide or to run.

Christmas

48   O troubled town of Bethlehem,
with conflict still you lie.
Above your deep but restless sleep
indifferent stars go by;
yet in your dark streets may you find
resilient, endless light:
for hopes and fears of all the years
were borne in you one night.

For Mary's child was born, and cried,
unnerving powers above,
while God of Life who shares our strife
encouraged hope and love.
O morning stars, now rocket-fire
obscures such hopeful births;
but mothers sing of everything –
their prayer still 'peace on earth'.

How silently, how violently,
your wondrous gift was given;
while God is grace for every race,
your streets with fear are riven.
As Jesus came amongst the poor
(confronting powers-that-be),
through risen will and faith he still
invites us 'Set them free.'

O daring child of Bethlehem,
empower us all, we pray,
to work for peace that wars may cease
and love be born today.
With all the nations' angels
proclaiming, we shall tell:
'Heal Bethlehem, join "us" with "them"' –
Amen, Immanuel!

Graham Adams (1975–)

Metre: CMD
Suggested Tune: FOREST GREEN

Epiphany

49 God, bless us as we celebrate this strange but hopeful feast,
and welcome those who journey now like sages from the east,
who search for truth in things above yet find it in 'the least':
O come, hidden king of humble birth, for the earth,
O help us learn and love all people's worth.

Reminding us that Christ was born to heal our wounds and scars,
the wise men came from foreign lands: outsiders with their stars;
that we may be one human race, let down our ancient guards:
O come, hidden king of humble birth, for the earth,
O help us learn and love all people's worth.

Prepare us, too, like those who came, to grasp surprising news;
that Christ was even born a king, though not as we might choose:
hands open, not enforcing peace, but risking being used:
O come, hidden king of humble birth, for the earth,
O help us learn and love all people's worth.

True now as then, our Herods fear the Prophet's faith newborn –
all those who dare to demonstrate the world shall be transformed;
so help us face inhuman ways, resist and not conform:
O come, hidden king of humble birth, for the earth,
O help us learn and love all people's worth.

As in their dreams, O God, reveal new paths for us to tread;
may we be wise enough to change our way, as they were led:
wise men and women sharing gifts which point to what's ahead:
O come, hidden king of humble birth, for the earth,
O help us learn and love all people's worth.

Graham Adams (1975–)

Metre: 14 14 14. and Refrain
Suggested Tune: GOD REST YOU MERRY

The life and ministry of Jesus

50   O Jesus, calm me as you calmed the storm,
         enfold me in your love, save me from harm;
         protect me till the tumults in me cease,
         remind me I am grounded in your peace.

         O Jesus, know me as you knew the one
         who reached out to you when all hope had gone,
         and touching just your hem found life renewed;
         remind me I am always known by you.

         O Jesus, hear me as you came to hear
         the one whose noise was such few dared come near;
         turn to me so I know you see my face,
         and in my fear I find a holy place.

         Anne Sardeson (1966–)

Inspired by words by David Adam ('Border Lands', SPCK, 1991):

         Calm me, O Lord, as you stilled the storm.
         Still me, O Lord, keep me from harm.
         Let all the tumult within me cease.
         Enfold me, Lord, in your peace.

Metre: 10 10.10 10.
Tune: CALM (Sardeson)

CALM

Anne Sardeson (1966–)

O Je - sus, calm me as you calmed the storm, en -
-fold me in your love, save me from harm; pro -
-tect me till the tu -mults in___ me cease,___ re -
-mind me I am ground-ed in your peace.___

The life and ministry of Jesus

51   We turn from those who fill us with disgust
and shrink from those we do not understand.
We only deal with some because we must,
failing to make response to their demand.
Yet, moved to tears by a leper's trust,
Christ reached and touched him with a loving hand.

God, help us see the world as through your eyes,
to be aware of those who need your care;
to be compassionate, not worldly-wise;
to hear their pleas for help and meet you there.
Then, with your touch of love to heal their lives,
those disregarded ones know answered prayer.

Marjorie Dobson (1940–)

Based on Mark 1:40–45

Metre: 10.10.10.10.10.10.
Suggested Tune: UNDE ET MEMORES

The life and ministry of Jesus

52   The touch was so light that it passed by unnoticed.
      The crowd was so dense, who could possibly tell
      that there in the crush was a desperate woman,
      a woman entombed by her personal hell.

      The touch was so light and yet someone had noticed –
      the man at the centre; the man in demand;
      the healer whose presence was urgently sought for
      a child who was needing the power from his hand.

      The touch turned his head as he wondered who'd done it.
      The poor guilty woman was bowed by her shame.
      But power had gone from him, he knew he was needed.
      With fear she admitted that she was to blame.

      The touch of his robe had already proved healing.
      The sound of his voice was a blessing at last.
      'My daughter, take courage, your suffering is over.
      Your pain and disgrace are a part of your past.'

      One touch in a crowd had seemed pointless to others
      and many felt agony at the delay.
      But one outcast woman could be well for ever
      and others would know that same touch on that day.

      Marjorie Dobson (1940–)

© Copyright 2017 Stainer & Bell Ltd

Based on Mark 5:24–34 and Luke 8:42–48

Metre: 12.11.12.11.
Suggested Tune: STREETS OF LAREDO

The life and ministry of Jesus

53   Walking through the town that day,
crowds surrounding them,
woman reaches out her hand
and touches Jesus' hem.
Years spent, money spent, hope spent –
only now her bleeding healed.

His disciples saw just masses,
jostling, pushing to
see and hear the healing man
doing something new.
Trust risked, safety risked, shame risked –
only now a blessing sealed.

Jesus was amazed to learn
he need not choose one
to cure and assemble whole.
Power claimed and done.
Live well, live blest, live whole –
her faith now for all revealed.

Janet Eldred (1957–)

Based on Mark 5:24–34 and Luke 8:42–48

Metre: 7.5.7.5.7.7.
Tune: KREACH

KREACH

Damian Boddy (1948–)

Walk-ing through the town that day, crowds sur-round-ing them, wo-man reach-es out her hand and touch-es Je-sus' hem. Years spent, mo-ney spent, hope spent – on-ly now her bleed-ing healed. -ealed.

The life and ministry of Jesus

54   When exhausted by the crowds
and so in need of rest,
Jesus and his friends went in
as someone else's guest.
But a foreign woman came,
though we do not know her name,
and she played a feisty game,
and proved that she knew best.

For her daughter was not well
and needed healing 'now!'
So she came to Jesus, but
at first he turned her down.
His reply appears his worst,
for he put his own kind first,
which of course ignored her thirst
for healing needed 'now!'

So she dared to argue on:
'But even dogs get fed.'
Shaming Jesus for his view
she turned it on its head.
And amazingly he knew,
so he 'shamed' himself more too:
for he saw her vision through –
that all should 'now' be fed.

Graham Adams (1975–)

Based on Mark 7:24–30

Metre: 7.6.7.6.7 7 7.6.
Suggested Tune: KELVINGROVE

The life and ministry of Jesus

55 Weeping woman, widowed, wailing –
all her life, men round her ailing.
Now, with grief, her own heart failing.
Who can help at times like this?

Husband died, though not long married.
Now her son is coffin-carried.
From now on her life is arid.
Who can help at times like this?

Though a crowd was there to hide her,
Jesus moved to be beside her,
knew the fear that terrified her.
He must help at times like this.

Woman, wide-eyed with misgiving,
could not know what God was giving,
till she saw her son now living.
God can help at times like this.

Crisis times may overtake us;
illness or bereavement shake us;
God is there; will not forsake us.
God will help at times like this.

Marjorie Dobson (1940–)

Based on Luke 7:11–17

Metre: 8 8 8.7.
Suggested Tune: QUEM PASTORES

The life and ministry of Jesus

56   We follow Christ, who leads the way,
though faithfulness is held at bay,
for we are held by unseen things
which tend to make us want to stay;
but, when he comes to teach his art,
may he lead us by hand and heart.

We follow Christ – but are surprised
he lays saliva on our eyes
to heal our vision of the things
which hold us back, so we may rise:
but we see walking trees, to start;
becoming human glimpsed in part.

We follow Christ, who tries again
to open eyes and minds – and then
we see each other's being whole
and work with him, with heart and soul,
not going back the way we knew
but daring now to see it through.

So may our vision be restored
as we keep seeing Christ as Lord,
though not so we neglect our part
but join with him, with hands and heart,
that we may see how we can be
Christ-like in our humanity.

Graham Adams (1975–)

Based on Mark 8:22–26

Metre: 8 8.8.8.8 8.
Suggested Tunes: SUSSEX CAROL; MELITA

Maundy Thursday

57   A towel and a basin?
This caused them great unease.
Their Master, now a servant?
The Christ upon his knees?
In washing feet made dirty
out on the city street,
he showed the power of action
where love and duty meet.

Yet Peter made his protest
and missed the point again,
till Jesus told him gently
that he must share his pain.
They hardly understood him,
although his words were clear
and soon his wise example
would be wiped out by fear.

But later they remembered
and took his words to heart:
in sacrifice and service
they gave the church its start,
and we who follow after
take up the task today,
to show, in love and service,
we also walk Christ's way.

Marjorie Dobson (1940–)

Metre: 7.6.7.6.D.
Suggested Tune: SALLEY GARDENS

Around the table

58   In the home that makes us welcome, with a door that opens wide,
offering warmth and light and comfort to all those who step inside;
in the giving and the sharing, making free of sacred space,
God invites both host and stranger with the tenderness of grace.

We give thanks for joyful sharing, for the love that longs to give,
sharing food in free abundance, room to breathe, and space to live.
In the gentle place of quietness, that gives ease to wounded souls,
God invites both host and stranger to a love that makes us whole.

In the patterns that disturb us and disrupt our ordered days,
in the challenges of questions calling us to different ways;
in the risk and mess of sharing, in the anger and the hurt,
God invites both host and stranger to the hope that gives new birth.

God of welcome, God of sharing, God of hope and risk and pain,
in the bread and wine you offer, we drink deep of loss and gain.
In the joy of humble giving, in the promises of prayer,
you are there, both host and stranger, hands outstretched to serve and care.

Jan Berry (1953–)

Metre: 15 15.15 15.
Tune: HOME
Alternative Tune: PICARDY

HOME

Anne Sardeson (1966–)

In the home that makes us wel - come, with a door that o - pens wide, offer - ing warmth and light and com - fort to all those who step in - side; in the giv - ing and the shar - ing, mak - ing free of sa - cred space, God in - vites both host and stran - ger with the ten - der - ness of grace.

Around the table: the Sanctus

59   Holy, holy, holy God,
           heaven and earth delight in your Wisdom;
           holy, holy, holy God,
           blessed be God's holy name.

           Blessed be the one who breaks bread with the hungry;
           blessed be the one who feasts with the poor.
           Blessed be the one who declares your love;
           blessed be God's holy name.

           Holy, holy, holy God,
           heaven and earth delight in your Wisdom;
           holy, holy, holy God,
           blessed be God's holy name.

           Jan Berry (1953–)

Tune: SANCTUS

SANCTUS

Jan Berry (1953–)

Ho - ly, ho - ly, ho - ly God, heav - en and earth de -light in your Wis - dom; ho - ly, ho - ly, ho - ly God, blessed be God's ho - ly name. Blessed be the one who breaks bread with the hun - gry; blessed be the one who feasts with the poor. Blessed be the one who de - clares your love; blessed be God's ho - ly name. Ho - ly, ho - ly, ho - ly God, heav - en and earth de - light in your Wis - dom; ho - ly, ho - ly, ho - ly God, blessed be God's ho - ly name.

The tune may be sung a cappella, or with the accompaniment of bells or chimes.

Around the table

60   As we gather round this table,
           mindful of the hurt we bring,
           God invites us to come closer,
           in his love – remembering.

           Bread is blessed and raised to heaven,
           gift of grace which makes love real;
           all the healing and forgiveness
           comes to us within this meal.

           Wine is poured, and offered to us,
           hands are open to receive;
           in the silence and the waiting
           love calls us and shapes belief.

           Ruth Dillon (1956–)

Metre: 8.7.8.7.
Suggested Tunes: SERVANT SONG; SHARON (Boyce)

Maundy Thursday: around the table

61 Shattered people round a table,
reaching out and taking bread,
thinking thoughts that they'll remember,
some things thought, but left unsaid.

Wine they drank was meant for sharing,
Jesus spoke of his own blood,
bread was broken, like his body,
were his friends now filled with dread?

Judas emphasised division,
they were not of just one mind,
they had argued and debated,
God would know what they would find.

Yet much later we re-member,*
bring this meal into today,
recollect through place and action,
through the words we sing and say.

Shattered people find new purpose,
energised, no more reviled,
fed by God, the once divided
find that we are reconciled.

Andrew Pratt (1948–)

* *The use of 're-member' with a hyphen suggests a 'putting back together'. The Greek word 'anamnesis', meaning 'remembrance', has this sense – of re-presenting or re-enacting the Last Supper.*

Metre: 8.7.8.7.
Suggested Tune: CROSS OF JESUS

The cross

62   In the depth of human suffering
in the mystery of loss,
in the cry of desolation
we are walking with the cross.

When our hearts are sore and aching,
grieving, weary with the strain,
God walks with us, bearing witness
to the love that holds our pain.

When relationships are broken,
and the ties of trust are torn,
God walks with us, bearing witness
in the wait for hope newborn.

In a world of hurt and violence,
bodies broken and abused,
God walks with us, bearing witness
to the longing search for truth.

When our world is spoiled and damaged,
air polluted, beauty marred,
God walks with us, bearing witness
to the tending of earth's scars.

In and through creation's suffering
in the mystery of loss,
on the road of our redemption
God is walking with the cross.

Jan Berry (1953–)

Metre: 8.7.8.7.
Suggested Tunes: MARCHING; KINGDOM (Copes)

The cross (Stabat mater)

63   *Bye, bye, bye, bye! I hear you cry,*
           my son, my dearest one!

Hard by a cross a mother stands
as her beloved hangs.
The piercing sword within her breast
recalls her birthing pangs.
Refrain

Scapegoat for culture's greed and spite,
he bears the scourge's scars.
She contemplates those weeping wounds
while Jesus' life departs.
Refrain

Christic compassion swells her heart;
may we in love draw near,
and touch with her the suffering Christ,
the piercing of the spear.
Refrain

Mary of Wisdom, shower your grace
on all our cosmic pain.
Enwrap, enfold, empower with love,
bring us to health again.
Refrain

Strongest of women, send us strength;
I would lament with you
and feel the dying pain of Christ;
through it I'll be renewed.
Refrain

So when I leave this fleeting life
I'll recognise your Son.
In all who share life's hurts and hate
with you to him I'll come.
Refrain

June Boyce-Tillman (1943–)

The first half of the tune is used for the refrain and the words echo those of the original.
The verse requires the whole tune.

Metre: CM and Refrain
Suggested Tune: COVENTRY CAROL

Easter, in the garden

64   When earth is cold, and frosty ground lies sleeping,
          when nothing grows, and all the world seems bare,
          then in our lostness, love comes to our weeping;
          in all our longing, Christ, you seek us there.

          When earth grows green, and buds begin to open,
          and hope peeps out, the fresh new shoots of spring,
          in the still moment, when the world is hoping,
          we wake to find the joy that morning brings.

          When in the garden, risen Christ, we meet you,
          with recognition dawning on our pain,
          in fragile trust, with wondering love we greet you
          and know that Wisdom dances once again.

          When spring breaks out, in colour and in glory,
          and beauty flourishes in dazzling light,
          we sing the truth and mystery of the story,
          with alleluias ringing in delight.

          Jan Berry (1953–)

Metre: 11.10.11.10.
Suggested Tune: FINLANDIA

4

HEALING IN LIFE'S TRANSITIONS

Ask someone to name a hymn that is meaningful to them, and often they will choose one that is linked to a particular time in their lives, or to an experience of transition. It may be one that was sung at one of the traditional rites of passage: a baptism, or a wedding, or a funeral. Or perhaps they will remember hymns that were significant for them at a particular moment of change or loss, or when they were about to embark on a new venture.

Healing is not restricted to times of physical illness and suffering. It is an ongoing process throughout our lives, as we discover more of God's loving purpose of wholeness. In anxiety or fear about the unknown, in the excitement and challenge of new beginnings or callings, in the pain and grief of bereavement, and in the wisdom and the difficulties of ageing and death, we seek God's healing grace. God is there not only to carry us through pain, but also to nurture us as we grow and flourish.

Many of the hymns in this section were written in relation to specific contexts, often as gifts or in response to a request. Whilst these are noted, the hymns here are written in such a way that they can be used more widely, and can take us through the seasons and cycles of our lives in an assurance of God's promise that whatever life brings, 'all shall be well'.

For the death of a new baby within a family

65   We cradled you with blessing,
as your parents' teardrops blurred.
A child we named for laughter
where joy must stay unheard.

We carried you with grieving;
hold your siblings to create
a squealing playful laughter,
for life will never wait.

We buried you caressing,
caught your memory in a game
and smiled remembering laughter,
where love has caught the pain.

We blessed you with conceiving,
left our memories untold
and strained to hear the laughter,
as missing years unfold.

Craig Muir (1961–)

Metre: 7.7.7.6.
Tune: CRADLE

CRADLE

Anne Sardeson (1966–)

We___ cradl - ed you with bless - ing, as your___ pa - rents' tear - drops blurred. A___ child we named for laugh - ter where_ joy must stay un - heard.

For an infant baptism or dedication

66   In trust receiving all that hope offers,
in faith believing, we find your grace.
God of love, greet us with words of welcome;
lovingly meet us, here in this place.

In all our growing, risking and learning,
your truth is showing how to be free.
God of beginnings, teach us your wisdom,
show us the meaning that's yet to be.

Music and singing tell of your wonder,
harmony ringing deep in our hearts.
God of our playing, with shape and colour,
we bring our praying, in making art.

Life's path lies open, stretching before us;
blessing and hoping mark each new day.
God of tomorrow, in all our searching,
help us to follow your living way.

Jan Berry (1953–)

Metre: 10.9.10.9.
Tune: BUSNENSA
Alternative Tune: BUNESSAN

BUSNENSA

Valerie Ruddle (1932–)

Celebrating an adoption/baptism

67 O God, whose tenderness shines bright
through all our darkest days,
you gather us into the light,
you make us laugh in pure delight
and wonder at your ways.

O God, who walks with us each day
exploring all that's new,
you join with us in joyful play,
you travel with us on our way,
discovering what's true.

O God, who knows our aching care,
the heartbreak and the pain,
you listen to our longing prayer,
you fill our lives with love to share,
so hope springs up again.

O God, who holds us on your knee
and gives us space to grow,
your daring love that sets us free
helps us to be all we can be,
yet never lets us go.

We find you, God, in every place
however far we roam;
we move into an open space,
your promise leads us on in grace,
until you bring us home.

Jan Berry (1953–)

Metre: 8.6.8 8.6.
Suggested Tune: REPTON

For children

68   Can the parents' tender care
cease towards the child they bear?
Yes, and we stand by and see
sadnesses and cruelty.

*When the bells of Christmas ring,
we recall a savage king,
who killed children in his spite;
we today still share that night:

Children trafficked, parents killed,
childhood's promise unfulfilled,
children naked, poor and cold,
children who will not grow old.

Child abuse is wounding Christ;
children's armies pierce his side;
children's worries fill God's heart;
where can God's forgiveness start?

God of parents, carers, friends,
teach us how to make amends;
bless our aims, forgive our wrongs,
help our children sing your songs.

June Boyce-Tillman (1943–)

* The second verse may be omitted.

Metre: 7 7.7 7.
Suggested Tune: BUCKLAND

About abuse

69 When we see love contorted and embattled
amidst the trash and rubble of our world,
entwined with guilt unmerited and twisted,
our hearts cry out, obscenities are hurled.
Creator God, will you respond with kindness,
or are your ears stopped and your tight lips curled?

When sweet endearment leads to monstrous violence
and hopes are dashed and gentle trust is bruised,
and power misused and weaknesses exploited
and youth's naiveté hurt and accused,
deep God of Love, are you within our struggling?
Can you be found in actions of abuse?

We long to hope that good at last will triumph
and flowers grow from out the harrowed wounds;
can resurrection joy transfigure darkness
and shape harsh crying into beauty's tunes?
Redeeming power, flow out from Jesus' story,
infuse our terror, find in us a room.

Protect us from a premature forgiveness,
from preachers' words that reinforce the pain,
from glib dogmatic institution statements
that crush bright anger's liberating flame;
so when in time the kairos moment beckons
we will find trust in humankind regained.

In telling stories, listening and acceptance,
may we perceive the action of your grace;
your living shows love's crucifixion strangeness,
how contradictions dwell in time and space;
great God of questions, paradox and mystery,
your Being holds us in this sacred place.

June Boyce-Tillman (1943–)

Metre: 11.10.11.10.11.10.
Suggested Tune: FINLANDIA

For a birthday celebration

70   We offer thanks for all life's gifts,
for friends and home, and carefree days;
for quiet rest that calms our nights,
and plans and dreams that guide our ways.
We look in trust for what will come,
with words that stumble into prayer;
we step out on the unseen path,
and find your wisdom waiting there.

We stand here on this edge of time,
with all that's shaped and formed our years;
the dreams and hurt, the loss and gains,
the fun, the laughter, and the tears.
And when in illness, grief, or pain,
we feel our lives are put on hold,
with care and faithfulness of friends,
in love and hope the story's told.

Like seeds that fall into the soil,
we grow into the green of spring,
when lives rebuild and gardens bloom,
and joyfully our voices sing.
And when the journey leads us home,
where welcome waits, and barriers fall,
we find you in creation's depth,
the mystery at the heart of all.

Jan Berry (1953–)

Metre: LMD
Suggested Tune: YE BANKS AND BRAES

Celebrating God's call/ordination

71   You have opened up for me a space
of joy and delight for all to see;
with wonder I receive your grace,
as I take the way you've shown to me.

I know that you are by my side,
and in your call I'm finding me;
with humble confidence and pride,
I'm walking the way you walk with me.

I am cheered on by the love and prayer
of people who have made me free;
they wave their pompoms in the air
as I dance the way you've cleared for me.

I am coming home with a spring in my step,
to the place where I am meant to be;
and in your tender strength I'm kept,
as I walk the way you've shaped for me.

Jan Berry (1953–)

Metre: Irregular
Suggested Tune: THE WRAGGLE-TAGGLE GYPSIES, O

For a time of transition or interim ministry

72   In our searching for a harbour,
      striking out for solid ground,
      threatened by the storm clouds looming,
      and the waves that crash around;
      help us see your star above us,
      guiding to a goal that's true.
      God, who knows the wind that's blowing,
      hold us on our course to you.

      When we know the pain of struggle,
      stumbling with the words for prayer,
      reaching out with hope of healing,
      weighted with our load of care;
      in your loving presence with us,
      in the tenderness of grace,
      Christ, who knows our fragile hurting,
      hold us safe in your embrace.

      In that moment on the threshold,
      pausing till the time to go,
      in the tension of our waiting
      for a world we do not know;
      with our hands outstretched in longing
      for a hope that's yet unseen,
      Spirit, with us in each moment,
      hold us in the space between.

      Trinity of awe and wonder,
      bringing faith and dreams to birth,
      breathing life through all that's living,
      God of all in heaven and earth:
      in your all-surrounding Wisdom,
      making holy every place,
      Maker, Christ and Holy Spirit,
      hold the world in your embrace.

      Jan Berry (1953–)

Metre: 8.7.8.7.D.
Suggested Tune: SCARLET RIBBONS

After an operation

73   Articulated bony joints and flexing muscle strength
reveal your rich creative mind within this earth's terrain;
we give you thanks for movement's grace and hands that touch and heal,
for sport and dance and walking frames and vibrant surgeon's skill.
For the neck bone's connected to the back bone,
and the back bone's connected to the hip bone,
and the hip bone's connected to the knee bone;
Oh! hear the Word of the Lord.

The blissful heights of deepest joy and forests of despair
exist within your loving heart and exercise your care;
we give you thanks for empathy, companionship and friends
and nets of prayer and ways to cope with all that life can send.
Chorus

While angels soar in singing clouds and orchestras of sound,
beneath earth's crust the ants and bugs plough up the fertile ground;
we give you thanks for cosmic flow through diverse varied forms
and listen for celestial choirs and smoothly tunnelling worms.
Chorus

Within this globe we can create communities that heal,
re-weave within embodied selves your Spirit's touch and feel;
we give you thanks for strengthening love that holds us in your hands
and pray that we may bring to birth connecting cosmic bands.
Chorus

June Boyce-Tillman (1943–)

The tune adapts the folksong 'Dives and Lazarus' for the verse, and the spiritual 'Dem Bones' by James Weldon Johnson (1871–1938) for the chorus.

Metre: 14 14.14 14. and Chorus
Tune: HYMN INCARNATION

HYMN INCARNATION

Adapted June Boyce-Tillman (1943–)

Ar - ti - cu - la - ted— bo - ny joints and— flex - ing— mus - cle— strength re - veal your rich cre - a - tive mind with- -in this— earth's ter - rain; we give you thanks for— move-ment's grace and— hands that— touch and— heal, for— sport and dance and— walk - ing frames and— vi - brant— sur - geon's skill.

CHORUS

For the neck bone's con - nect - ed to the back bone, and the back bone's con - nect - ed to the hip bone, and the hip bone's con - nect - ed to the knee bone; Oh! hear the Word of the Lord.

In times of uncertainty

74   One step enough? We question what we know
and seek for knowledge yet beyond our grasp.
Uncertainty can make us insecure,
we thirst for trusted knowledge that will last.

We live within a finite span of time,
this planet is the only earth we know.*
When people talk of God we are not sure:
as faith and doubt are balanced, which will grow?

But all we know is bound by space and time,
however much we struggle to be free,
and somehow we have reached this point in time,
which once was future that we could not see.

Some inner strength or God has helped us move,
has brought us to this time in which we stand;
and in this span of now and in between,
God guide us, with your holy human hand.

Andrew Pratt (1948–)

* *'The only earth we know' is a phrase borrowed by the author from the work of Fred Kaan.*

Metre: 10.10.10.10.
Tune: UNCERTAINTY

UNCERTAINTY

Anne Sardeson (1966–)

One step e-nough? We ques-tion what we know and seek for know-ledge yet be-yond our grasp. Un-cer-tain-ty can make us in-se-cure, we thirst for trust-ed know-ledge that will last.

For retirement, or any move into a new situation

75   For all we've known, we offer up our praise:
caring and laughter which enriched our days,
colour and music, children, fun with friends –
and all the hurting which our loving mends.

When we are trudging on a narrow way,
hemmed in by pressures and demands each day,
struggling to find the space to dance and move,
help us to find our centre in your love.

Lead us into a wide and open space,
stretching into the freedom of your grace,
room so that we can breathe and change and grow,
learning to share the wisdom that we know.

Set out your table where we all are fed,
here empty hands receive the broken bread,
greeting each other as we come to share
life-giving Wisdom through our praise and prayer.

Jan Berry (1953–)

Metre: 10 10.10 10.
Suggested Tune: HIGHLAND CATHEDRAL

A hymn of thanks at a retirement service

76   In all the memories that our life has brought us,
of home and church, of families and friends,
yours is the love that wonderfully sought us,
filling our hearts with thanks that never end.

In all our serving, welcoming and giving,
seeking to show Christ's light for all to see,
yours is the love that shines through all our living,
offering the hope that sets your people free.

When life is dark, and threats and fears surround us,
in all the struggle, anger, pain and stress,
yours is the love that wraps strong arms around us,
embracing us to hold and heal and bless.

Trusting your promise, tracing your light's gleaming,
we move in faith into a new-found space;
yours is the love that leads beyond our dreaming,
to know the height and breadth and depth of grace.

Jan Berry (1953–)

Metre: 11.10.11.10.
Suggested Tune: O PERFECT LOVE

Ageing

77   When we're losing movement, sight,
         when our hopes and dreams take flight,
         in the fading of our powers,
         memories of brighter hours,
         God of all our days and years,
         weep with us and cry our tears.

         When we're sharing all we've learned,
         all the knowledge wisdom's earned,
         freed from burdens, tasks and cares,
         holding others in our prayers,
         God of all our work and skill,
         strengthen us in mind and will.

         In our journey to be free,
         reaching out to what will be,
         searching out our future ways,
         grasping life with joyful praise,
         God of all our hopes and plans,
         dance with us and take our hands.

         When we're losing touch with friends,
         and sustaining contact ends,
         when we gaze at all that's past,
         offering thanks for love that lasts,
         God who lives in bone and breath,
         be with us in life, in death.

         Jan Berry (1953–)

Metre: 7 7.7 7.7 7.
Tune: GOD OF ALL
Alternative Tune: DIX

GOD OF ALL

Valerie Ruddle (1932–)

When we're los - ing move - ment, sight, when our
hopes and dreams take flight, in the fad - ing of our
powers, me - mo - ries of brigh - ter hours, God of all our
days and years, weep with us and cry our tears.

For carers

78   When our caring love wears thin,
when our nerves are stretched and taut
and the strain of our concern
fills our every waking thought –
God of understanding heart,
give us strength to play our part.

When we watch in helpless love
when all hope of health is past
and distress cries out in pain
that this suffering will not last –
God of healing, hold us near,
bring your calm and drive out fear.

When our tears speak out our love,
when by smiles we mask our grief,
in those dark and lonely hours
when the silence mocks belief –
God of comfort, to our night
bring the dawning of your light.

*When the one we loved has gone,
when death brings tormented peace,
as emotions swirl around,
sorrow mingled with release –
God of patience, bear our pain;
turn us back to life again.

Marjorie Dobson (1940–)

* The last verse should be omitted if inappropriate.

Metre: 7.7.7.7.7 7.
Tune: GOD OF COMFORT

GOD OF COMFORT

Ian Sharp (1943–)

Ageing

79   With thoughts that wander, minds feel frail,
our being still intact,
we look with sad yet wondering eyes,
as memory echoes fact.

That past is real, not faded, lost:
it made us who we are,
but living in the present tense,
we neither rank, nor star.

Yet God, who knew us at our birth,
still folds in love and grace,
has brought us to this present day,
still knows each name and face.

And to this God we offer all
in faithful love and praise,
through singing laughter, wringing tears,
through every changing phase.

Andrew Pratt (1948–)

Metre: CM
Suggested Tune: IRISH

For a funeral

80   We greet each death in peace or apprehension,
assured through faith, or filled with doubt and fear.
Sometimes our laughter hides our consternation,
while salt tears flow, and flames of sorrow sear.

The image that we grasp enfolds such memories,
of love, of life, of every joy and pain;
we reminisce and sharing makes us stronger
to face the future, reach for life again.

We leave this moment; those who stand around us
go home and leave us standing here alone,
and we must go rejoining life's adventure,
to find the peace that we might hold and own.

Andrew Pratt (1948–)

Metre: 11.10.11.10.
Suggested Tune: INTERCESSOR

Death and dying

81   At one with God, at one with all creation.
           As yet we only taste the coming feast.
           Is death a time of health, of re-creation,
           when all our human wholeness is released?

           Is death the way we pass to human gladness,
           of life in all its fullness yet unfound,
           a way beyond our sadness and our grieving,
           a way to dance on holy, hallowed ground?

           Or are these words unhelpful speculation?
           Is this the only planet we might know?
           Whatever comes of all our exploration,
           love lives, will live beyond the here and now!

           Andrew Pratt (1948–)

Metre: 11.10.11.10.
Suggested Tune: FINLANDIA

For a funeral

82   We bring our gratitude to you
for guidance in our lives,
for those whose love has touched our hearts
and made our souls revive.

We bring our thanks for caring strength
that holds us on our way,
and brings us closer to your heart,
and drives our fear away.

For human hands can foster hope
and make our pathway clear,
support us in our weaknesses
and make your love come near.

We ask your blessing for these souls
as on through death they speed,
and pray that you will bless us too
with all the strength we need.

Our hearts are filled with healing love
and overflowing grace.
Our roots are formed by faith in you;
we feel your warm embrace.

June Boyce-Tillman (1943–)

Metre: CM
Suggested Tune: ST ANNE

For a funeral

83　The lives we mourn have known their share of heartache,
of human fear, uncertainty and shock,
and yet we also shared in love and laughter,
our memories hold solid as a rock;
for on through time remembrance will be treasured,
we'll keep it close when joy is tinged with pain,
we'll never lose the smiles that sign togetherness,
and day to day we know that love will still remain.

We never know what waits in life's uncertainty,
we never know what love, what joy, what fear
can build us up, or leave us lost and comfortless,
afraid to face, again, the coming year;
yet here are people who can hold their hands with us,
can walk with us into the great unknown,
and so together we can walk the path of life,
and know that when we stumble love will still be shown.

So take my hand, my friend, my neighbour, walk with me,
together we can face the passing storm,
and know with God, in spite of tears and emptiness,
there is a sense that new love can be born.
In this we trust, for through our grief God held to us,
and human arms once caught us when we fell,
beyond this day each dawn will bring new hope for us
that through God's love and grace and care all will be well.

Andrew Pratt (1948–)

Metre:　　　　　12.10.12.10.12.10.12.12.
Suggested Tune:　LONDONDERRY AIR

5

SINGING OUR PRAYERS

The familiar saying, attributed to St Augustine of Hippo, that 'whoever sings prays twice' usefully reminds us that in vocalising our prayers to God we add something unique to them. This value is recognised formally in many worshipping traditions, for example in the sung responses of Taizé or the Iona Community.

What exactly does such singing contribute? Perhaps it creates a stillness that sets us apart from our busyness. All too often our prayers get bogged down in our worthy words or in our desperate bidding and begging of God; but when we sing them we can still that frenetic activity, taking time to remind ourselves that, in our praying, we are often more in need of being changed ourselves than changing the mind of God.

Perhaps it makes a connection to something deep within us: words can often flash past us and fail to stay put and take root. Singing slows down our words and our thoughts. It offers a chance for a deeper connection with what lies both beyond and deep within us. Perhaps, too, it enhances the perspective of our vision. In *A Lever and a Place to Stand*, Richard Rohr talks of prayer as a lever on that which would overwhelm and defeat us; with the addition of music, prayer makes the 'lever' even stronger, for as we sing we can step back from whatever seems too much for us.

Prayer is a place to offer to God that which needs healing, and music takes us to a place of healing within us. Singing our prayers helps us to make the most of these two wonderful gifts.

Listen, Lord

LISTEN LORD   *Valerie Ruddle (1932–)*

84   Listen, Lord, and hear our song
            for those who cannot sing.

            Listen, Lord, and hear our words
            for those who cannot speak.

            Listen, Lord, and hear our plea
            for those who cannot pray.

            Valerie Ruddle (1932–)

A solo voice might sing a verse that would be repeated by all, followed by everyone humming the tune two or three times before the soloist begins the next verse. The following descant might be sung by the soloist during some of the humming:

Metre: 7.6.
Tune: LISTEN LORD

Jesus is calling

JESUS IS CALLING   *Valerie Ruddle (1932–)*

Jes - us   is   call - ing, 'Come   to   me   and

I_____   will   give_____   you   rest.'_____

85   Jesus is calling, 'Come to me and I will give you rest.'

Jesus is calling, 'Come to me for peace of mind today.'

Jesus is calling, 'Come to me to calm your troubled mind.'

Valerie Ruddle (1932–)

A solo voice might sing a verse that would be repeated by all, followed by everyone humming the tune two or three times before the soloist begins the next verse.

Tune: JESUS IS CALLING

Touch me, Lord

TOUCH ME LORD   *Valerie Ruddle (1932–)*

86   Touch me, Lord, with your healing hands,
        heal my pain.
        Touch me, Lord, with your healing hands,
        heal my pain.

        Touch me, Lord, with your soothing voice,
        give me peace.
        Touch me, Lord, with your soothing voice,
        give me peace.

        Touch me, Lord, with your gentle word,
        calm my mind.
        Touch me, Lord, with your gentle word,
        calm my mind.

        Touch me, Lord, with your constant love,
        hold my hand.
        Touch me, Lord, with your constant love,
        hold my hand.

        Valerie Ruddle (1932–)

The last three words of each verse could be 'hold my hand', which would enable a congregation that does not have copies of the words to join in.

Metre: 8.3.8.3.
Tune: TOUCH ME LORD

God who will release me

WINTER STILLNESS

Janet Eldred (1957–)

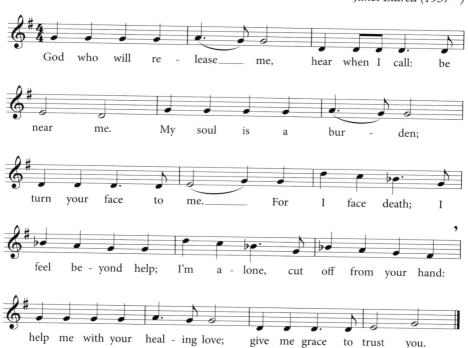

God who will re - lease___ me, hear when I call: be near me. My soul is a bur - den; turn your face to me.___ For I face death; I feel be - yond help; I'm a - lone, cut off from your hand: help me with your heal - ing love; give me grace to trust you.

87 God who will release me,
  hear when I call: be near me.
 My soul is a burden;
  turn your face to me.
   For I face death;
   I feel beyond help;
   I'm alone,
    cut off from your hand:
 help me with your healing love;
 give me grace to trust you.

Let me hear your voice today;
 my soul waits in silence.
Let me put my trust in you,
 refuge from my cares.
  For you are love
  and you are justice;
  you can hear
   my faithless crying:
save me with your healing love,
let me rest in your love.

Damian Boddy (1948–)

Based on Psalms 88 and 62.

Metre: Irregular
Tune: WINTER STILLNESS

I need you, Lord

88　In my darkness I need you, Lord,
in my brokenness I need you, Lord,
in my faithlessness I need you, Lord.
Where are you? I need you, Lord.

Tell me, Lord, where is heaven?
Tell me, Lord, what is heaven?
Tell me, Lord, where is peace?
Tell me, Lord, what is peace?

I lift my hands to find you, Lord.
I lift my heart to find you, Lord.
I lift my eyes to find you, Lord.
I lift my prayers to find you, Lord.

Pat Jones (1942–)

Metre:　Irregular
Tune:　　I NEED YOU LORD

I NEED YOU LORD

Pat Jones (1942–)

Hope and help

HOPE AND HELP   *Damian Boddy (1948–)*

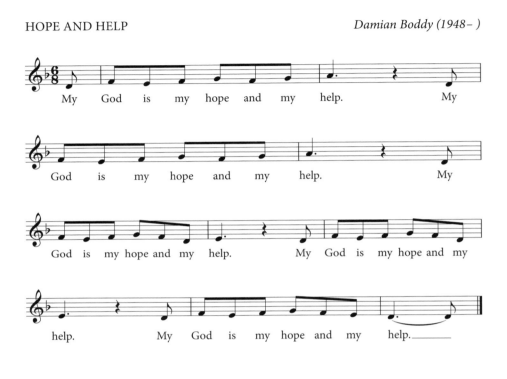

89   My God is my hope and my help.

My God is my hope and my help.

My God is my hope and my help.

My God is my hope and my help.

My God is my hope and my help.

Damian Boddy (1948–)

Tune: HOPE AND HELP

The quiet heart

THE QUIET HEART   *Myrna Michell (1951–)*

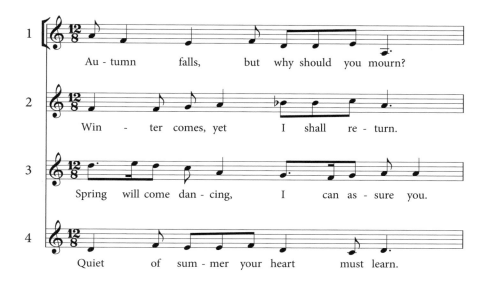

1. Au - tumn falls, but why should you mourn?
2. Win - ter comes, yet I shall re - turn.
3. Spring will come dan - cing, I can as - sure you.
4. Quiet of sum - mer your heart must learn.

90   Autumn falls, but why should you mourn?
Winter comes, yet I shall return.
Spring will come dancing, I can assure you.
Quiet of summer your heart must learn.

Myrna Michell (1951–)

Words and Music © Copyright 2017 Stainer & Bell Ltd

This piece may be used as a round or a chant.

Tune: THE QUIET HEART

River of healing

91   River of healing,
              river of life,
          holding us through the
              stresses and strife.
          River of healing,
              river of life.

          River of sunlight,
              river that flows
          through this life's dark days,
              easing its woes.
          River of sunlight,
              river that flows.

          River of comfort,
              river of might,
          lifting the senses
              back to the light.
          River of comfort,
              river of might.

          River of knowledge,
              river that yields,
          from earth's deep secrets
              new hope that heals.
          River of knowledge,
              river that yields.

          River of power,
              river of rest,
          blessing us all with
              strength for the test.
          River of power,
              river of rest.

          Jean Silvan Evans (1931–)

Metre: 5.4.5.4.5.4.
Tune: RIVER OF HEALING

RIVER OF HEALING

Sue Gilmurray (1950–)

Autumn leaves

AUTUMN LEAVES

L. J. Counsell (1949–)

Ba-lanc-ing life in the storms that sur-round us with hope,_____ not fear,_____ lis - ten to love in the wind and the sun, bring - ing wis - dom,_____ not fol - ly,_____ au - tumn leaves fall - ing like an - gels of heav - en, for heal - ing,_____ not hurt - ing._____ Al - le - lu - ia, al - le - lu - ia.

92 Balancing life in the storms that surround us with hope, not fear, listen to love in the wind and the sun, bringing wisdom, not folly, autumn leaves falling like angels of heaven, for healing, not hurting. Alleluia, alleluia.

L. J. Counsell (1949–)

This may be performed as a round, each voice entering after four bars.

Tune: AUTUMN LEAVES

Remembering

REMEMBERING

George Frideric Handel
Adapted June Boyce-Tillman (1943–)

God   of   the   cos - mos,   we   live   with - in   you,

hold   us,   em - brace   us   so   we___ can   be___ healed.

93   God of the cosmos, we live within you,
hold us, embrace us so we can be healed.

You are incarnate, tiny and helpless;
work with our weakness, so we can be healed.

You are a teacher, strengthening, empowering;
give us your courage, so we can be healed.

We would remember our shattered life dreams,
reshape their patterns so we can be healed.

Take all the fragments, bright ones and dark ones,
love them, sort through them, so we can be healed.

Your know our sadness; you know our glory;
lead us to Wisdom, so we can be healed.

June Boyce-Tillman (1943–)

Metre: 10.10.
Tune: REMEMBERING

Blessing be yours

94   Blessing be yours
               from the God who gives love,
           blessing be yours
               from the God who gives peace,
           blessing be yours
               from the God who gives joy,
           blessing be yours
               from the One in Three.

Ruth Dillon (1956–)

Tune: CRAIL

CRAIL

Ruth Dillon (1956–)

Bless - ing be yours from the God who gives love,
bless - ing be yours from the God who gives peace,
bless - ing be yours from the God who gives joy,_____

bless - ing be yours_ from the One_ in Three.

Bring wholeness, God

95   Bring wholeness, God, to those in pain,
whose life is frail as feathers.
    Surround them, God, in your *shalom*,
    where healing streams enfold them.

Bring wholeness, God, to those who grieve,
whose life is filled with tears.
    Surround them, God, in your *shalom*,
    where healing streams enfold them.

Bring wholeness, God, to those abused,
who feel the might of power.
    Surround them, God, in your *shalom*,
    where healing streams enfold them.

Bring wholeness, God, to those in need,
whatever need is present.
    Surround them, God, in your *shalom*,
    where healing streams enfold them.

Your *shalom*, God, brings harmony,
your gift of love for people.
    Your blessing flows like healing streams,
    to constantly enfold us.

Ruth Dillon (1956–)

Metre: 8.7.8.7.
Suggested Tune: ST COLUMBA

INDEX

INDEX OF FIRST LINES

First lines of choruses are shown in italic

INDEX OF TITLES

INDEX OF TUNE NAMES

Tunes printed in this anthology are marked with an asterisk

INDEX OF METRES

13 13.13 13.13 13.	14
14 13.13 13.13 13.	39
14 14 14. and Refrain	49
14 14.14 14. and Chorus	73
15 15.15 15.	58
Irregular	71, 87, 88

INDEX OF AUTHORS

INDEX OF COMPOSERS, ARRANGERS AND SOURCES

INDEX OF THEMES

Biblical characters are shown in italic

INDEX OF BIBLICAL REFERENCES

ACKNOWLEDGMENTS

The scripture quotation on page 22 is an extract from the Authorized Version of the Bible (The King James Bible), the rights in which are vested in the Crown, and is reproduced by permission of the Crown's Patentee, Cambridge University Press.

The quotation on page 66 is from David Adam's *Border Lands* and is reproduced by permission of SPCK, 36 Causton Street, London SWIP 4ST.